Gypsy Heart
Poetry

52 Week
Soul
Inspiring
Journal

JENNIFER CAIRO

Published by:

Powerful
Potential *Purpose*

PUBLISHING

Powerful Potential & Purpose Publishing
Website: www.PPP-publishing.com
Email: gloria@gloriacoppola.com

Design by Deborah Perdue, Illumination Graphics

ISBN 978-1-7349655-7-5

To all those who've inspired me
and didn't know it . . . .

Introduction

I've always had a love of books and reading, but
never expected to end up an author myself.
I would often put my thoughts down on paper, but
for years did nothing with them. Later in my adult
life, I found that writing became a therapy for me,
a way to express myself. The name Gypsy Heart
came to me in a dream, and I knew then this was
part of my journey as a writer. I am a gypsy heart;
it fits my personality, my style, and my eccentric
ways. I am a free spirit who's only just discovered
her true self . . .
I can finally let my inner gypsy free!

She's trouble
all wrapped up
in chaos and
impossible dreams . . .
with a sly smile
and a wicked way
about her
that will surely
drive you wild . . .

You can't help but love the Gypsy in her
Those wild eyes and mysterious smile
Her spirit grabs ahold of your soul
Making you want more
Her enchanting ways entice you, invite you
Come take her hand, don't fight it
Let her show you her magic
You can feel its power
Leaving you breathless, restless.
You can't wrap your mind around it
She has you where she wants you
A spell you're under
Thoughts of her take over
Setting her apart
How will you ever take your mind off
the girl with the Gypsy heart . . .

How can you manifest the life you desire?

_____

_____

_____

_____

_____

_____

_____

_____

_____

_____

_____

_____

_____

_____

_____

_____

She woke up stronger, wiser
and full of spark.
That was the day things changed . . .

*What will you do this week
to start heading towards your dreams?*

Sometimes in life you find out people
aren't who you thought they were.

Grow your roots.
Be your own strength.
You, and only you can make your dreams
come true . . .

What gives you strength?

She listens to the wind as it calls her name
Listening for the words she's longed to hear
Taking her back to a time that seemed so far away
Remembering the times that mattered most . . .

Listen to your intuition . . . what is it saying?

The ocean can be a place where you go to find
yourself, your true self
Let the waves strip down your layers
until you feel whole again
It may be painful, but this I promise
It will be worth it . . .

Where do you find the most peace?

_____

_____

_____

_____

_____

_____

_____

_____

_____

_____

_____

_____

_____

_____

_____

The moonlight makes her come alive
Bringing her to a place where few
have thought to go
Her wishes seem possible there
The quiet stillness . . . the peace it brings
Come sit with her and feel the magic . . .

What do you do to quiet your mind?

Spirituality means different things
to different people
You must feel the changes that happen to you
down to your soul
The growth, the pain, the beauty that becomes you
Only then can you transform into who you were
meant to be all along . . .

What does your spirituality mean to you?

_____

_____

_____

_____

_____

_____

_____

_____

_____

_____

_____

_____

_____

_____

_____

When you trust enough to allow yourself to be
vulnerable, you will open up doors that you never
knew possible.
Have patience with yourself as your experience
is part of your journey . . .

How will you open up doors for yourself?

She's the girl with the wild eyes and wild dreams
You can't tame the likes of her
She wants nothing more than to love hard
and be loved harder
Once she takes hold of your heart,
she'll never let go . . .

What makes your heart flutter? Adventure? Love?

_____

_____

_____

_____

_____

_____

_____

_____

_____

_____

_____

_____

_____

_____

_____

_____

_____

You get one chance at life, what will you do
with it?
Will you find the beauty in it
or will you let it pass you by?
Let today be the day you start living . . .

*If you had a chance to create the perfect life
for yourself, what would it look like?
What would be your first step?*

How deep are you willing to dig
to find yourself again?
Are you willing to get dirty and do the work?
What if what you find isn't what you expected,
but so much better?

When did you realize that there was more to you?

_____

_____

_____

_____

_____

_____

_____

_____

_____

_____

_____

_____

_____

_____

Sometimes people will hurt you.
They may never realize just how much.
It's your job to pick yourself up and keep going.
It's your responsibility to find your happiness.
You see, life has a funny way of trying to trip
you up.   That's part of the journey.
It doesn't always have to make sense.
Just know that everything you experience is part
of your path.
Find a way to embrace it and grow stronger . . .

How will you embrace life this week?

Wild one, there will be a time when you have
to settle down.
Life has plans for you.
Let your wild heart take you where you
are meant to be . . .

Where will you let your wild heart take you?

The fire that burns inside of you will keep you
going when you feel like quitting.
Don't you dare let this world crush your dreams!
It's meant for you to be heard
to make a difference, to shine brightly.
Go out there and make it happen . . .

What keeps your fire going?

There's something beautiful about a girl
who's not afraid to fall.
She can be brave and vulnerable all at once.
That untamed version of herself is exactly
what will save her.
Most won't know how to handle an energy
like hers,
and that is why she will make it.
Pure willingness to survive, to prove them
all wrong . . .

If you gave yourself a pep talk this week,
what would you say?

_____

_____

_____

_____

_____

_____

_____

_____

_____

_____

_____

_____

_____

_____

Losing your mind can be the best thing
that happens to you.
Sometimes hitting that low, the fear, the doubt, the
self hate will have no place to go.
It's where you get your chance to launch yourself
into greatness.
Just know that you will rise up out of the ashes,
stronger, wiser and unstoppable . . .

*You are unstoppable. Make a list of things
that no longer serve you and let them go.*

Don't let anyone tell you you're not good enough.
Don't you dare listen to them put you down.
Keep shining darling, the right one will find you
and love you for the tangled mess that you are . . .

We are all messy,
write down what makes you different.

_____

_____

_____

_____

_____

_____

_____

_____

_____

_____

_____

_____

_____

_____

_____

Make your wishes with all your might . . .

If you had three wishes, what would they be?

Maybe things happen for a reason,
Maybe you're not ready,
maybe you've missed your chance,
Try surrendering it all and let go
How about for once in your life
you just trust that the universe
Knows you better than you know yourself . . .

What do you fear about surrendering?

Every girl deserves a fairytale
Don't you dare settle for less
Someone will come along and love you
just the way you are
Forget changing for anyone
You are perfection the way you are . . .

Create your fairytale . . . what would it look like?

_____

_____

_____

_____

_____

_____

_____

_____

_____

_____

_____

_____

_____

_____

What does love feel like?
Does it feel like the ocean breeze?
What does love look like?
Does it look like the colors of the sunset?
What does love sound like?
Does it sound the waves crashing onto the shore?
What does love taste like?
Does it taste like a kiss in the rain?
Love can be what you make it
An explosion between two souls . . .

What does love feel like to you?

_____

_____

_____

_____

_____

_____

_____

_____

_____

_____

_____

_____

_____

_____

_____

*What are you going to make of yourself
in this world?
Will you be remembered by your tragedies?
Or
Will you be remembered by your greatness?*

The world needs you.
What can you do for someone this week?

_____

_____

_____

_____

_____

_____

_____

_____

_____

_____

_____

_____

_____

_____

There's nothing more beautiful than looking into
the eyes of an animal
That instant connection to their soul
The compassion, the feeling, the beauty
Something we don't always see in humans
Cherish the love you feel from them
It's rare, and it's beautiful . . .

How do animals make you feel?

They will never understand the wildness
in your soul
You see, you're not like them
There is something magical within you, a light
that shines that only few will ever see
That is why you are so special my dear
You're the one that makes dreams come true . . .

What gives you that spark, that drive to succeed?

Quiet your mind, calm your spirit
Listen to your guides
They will guide you, trust them
When you surrender to what is means to be, the
most beautiful life will be waiting
right in front of you . . .

Do you have guides? Do you let them guide you?

_____

_____

_____

_____

_____

_____

_____

_____

_____

_____

_____

_____

_____

_____

Music does something to your soul
You can get lost in it, feel every note and heal
from listening to it
It can be there for you when you're sad, happy or
in love
It's the friend when you're lonely
It's the rebel you long to be . . .

How do you connect with music?
Can you feel it down to your soul?

Let them wonder about you
They can't help themselves
It's hard to grasp your magic
Sure, they'll talk about you and that's ok
Just smile at them and walk away . . .

Walking away is hard. Have you ever had to walk away from someone?

_____

_____

_____

_____

_____

_____

_____

_____

_____

_____

_____

_____

_____

_____

Write your own story
You have everything it takes to make it happen
Use your gifts to inspire others, they are waiting
for something
Something to hold on to, to relate to, to believe in . . .

What gifts do you have to share with the world?

Spending time alone doesn't mean you are lonely
It means you are brave enough to sit
with your own thoughts
And that is something you should be proud of
As everyone has some darkness tucked away . . .

How do you feel about being alone?

_____

_____

_____

_____

_____

_____

_____

_____

_____

_____

_____

_____

_____

_____

The one thing that doesn't stop is time
Don't waste a second, enjoy every moment,
make memories, make it count . . .

How can you better manage your time this week?

It's the special ones who make you see clearly
To help you see yourself in a new light,
To push you to believe in yourself, to fight and
claw your way out of the darkness
Those special ones sometimes aren't in your life for
long however they will never be forgotten . . .

Who was there for you at your lowest?
Are they still a part of your life?

Nature can do many things
It can listen to all of your secrets,
It can hold all of your pain
When you go there to find yourself,
You may never come back again . . .

Where do you go to find yourself?

_____

_____

_____

_____

_____

_____

_____

_____

_____

_____

_____

_____

_____

_____

_____

Even the sweetest souls have a dark side
Waiting silently for a chance to show the world
just who they are messing with . . .

What are some things that you are holding on to that you can try to release?

_____

_____

_____

_____

_____

_____

_____

_____

_____

_____

_____

_____

_____

Meditation doesn't have to be perfect
As long as you set an intention with a pure heart
the universe will hear you . . .

Try a new meditation this week.

Decide what you want with your life and do it
If something doesn't feel right, run the other way
You only get one chance to make things happen . . .

What makes you feel uncomfortable?

Guess what?
Life is going to keep happening whether or not
you are happy
It's time to start living it
Find something that makes your soul shine
and enjoy the ride . . .

What makes your soul shine?

One day she realized we travel alone on this road
Through the many twists and turns, there will be
lessons learned, tears shed, layers stripped away of
the many hurts that she's endured
But just know this
At the end of that road she will be stronger
than ever before . . .

List some things that have made you strong.

_____

_____

_____

_____

_____

_____

_____

_____

_____

_____

_____

_____

_____

Beautiful crow keeps watch over me
Sending messages so I can see
I hear him call me late at night
Keeping me within his sight . . .

Do you have messengers? Write about them.

_____

_____

_____

_____

_____

_____

_____

_____

_____

_____

_____

_____

_____

_____

_____

_____

Solitude is a state of mind
There is both beauty and madness in the quietness
Are you afraid of it? Excited by it?
Let me tell you this
Once you can face it, all of it
Magic awaits . . .

Do you believe in magic?

_____

_____

_____

_____

_____

_____

_____

_____

_____

_____

_____

_____

_____

_____

*Strength doesn't mean there are no tears
In fact, strength means that you can wipe away
those tears and keep moving forward even if you
don't know what you're heading for . . .*

*What fears do you have in front of you this week?
Take on one challenge at a time!*

Make peace with the sorrow
Make peace with the pain
Understand it all has a purpose
To make you whole again . . .

What brings you peace?

© Brandon Montgomery

Look at all of those adventures waiting for you
You can see them there; they are so very beautiful
and enticing
Don't be afraid to take the first step,
trust in yourself
for once in your life
You are exactly where you need to be
The universe planned this for you
so fly with the wings
that you've kept hidden for so long . . .

This is a week for adventures.
What is something new that you can do this week?

That stirring that you feel inside of you
It's your passion, your fire
You can't ignore the calling that you have so much
more to share with the world . . .

What's your passion? This is the week to ignite it!

_____

_____

_____

_____

_____

_____

_____

_____

_____

_____

_____

_____

_____

_____

Starting over doesn't have to be scary
It can be a new adventure filled with excitement
and beauty
New places to explore
Don't fear the changes you're making
Sometimes the best things come from taking chances . . .

Set out to make a new friend this week.
Start with a simple "hello."

Soul to soul
Heart to heart
Fell in love
Never apart . . .

Do you believe your soul guides you?

They told her she couldn't do it
To be the person, she was meant to be
What they didn't expect is her drive
to make things happen
There's no stopping a girl like that . . .

You are unstoppable. List some goals for the week.

_____

_____

_____

_____

_____

_____

_____

_____

_____

_____

_____

_____

_____

_____

_____

_____

Simple minds will tell you, you can't do it
They will want you to fail
To be less than them
They cast their spells of doubt
They didn't count on your powerful will
To do more than just survive . . .

Write down your goals and crush them!

Dare to wish for
What you dream of
Love that fills your heart
Peace that warms your soul
Health, wealth and freedom
You can have it all . . .

What do you wish for?
How can you make your wishes come true?

_____

_____

_____

_____

_____

_____

_____

_____

_____

_____

_____

_____

_____

_____

Be the girl
With big dreams
And a kind heart . . .

What is your biggest dream?

Summer-time has a way of making us feel alive
Those magical summer nights
with fireflies and skies
full of stars . . .

What makes you feel alive?

Everyone needs a soulmate
A person to laugh and cry with
Go through life with
Once you find them, hold on tight
They may only come by once in a lifetime . . .

What would your perfect soulmate be like?

_____

_____

_____

_____

_____

_____

_____

_____

_____

_____

_____

_____

_____

_____

A *gypsy* is a mysteriously beautiful woman
who is provocative and sexy. Like the goddess, she
exudes the energy of passion, authenticity and
enthusiasm. You will find it hard to lock her down.
Her free spirit is prone to follow an unconventional
path. No matter what happens in life her goddess
energy is naturally in a state of joy, peace,
happiness and gratitude. Her mysterious and
seductive charm captures those who engage with
her. Unlock your goddess heart. The world is yours,
go out there and create the life you deserve.

Your life is a blank canvas and you hold
the brush!

A new year awaits you filled with hopes
and dreams.

Go out there and make it all happen!

You have everything that you need, and like
the girl with the Gypsy heart,
you will make your dreams a reality!

I believe in you!

XOXO

A space to let your inner gypsy goddess explore and create her path

_____

_____

_____

_____

_____

_____

_____

_____

_____

_____

_____

_____

_____

_____

_____

A space to let your inner gypsy goddess explore and create her path

---

A space to let your inner gypsy goddess explore and create her path

---

---

*A space to let your inner gypsy goddess explore and
create her path*

*A space to let your inner gypsy goddess explore and
create her path*

_____

_____

_____

_____

_____

_____

_____

_____

_____

_____

_____

_____

_____

_____

_____

A space to let your inner gypsy goddess explore and create her path

Photographer Credits

Terry McLain Art Collections
www.fineartamerica.com

Brandon Montgomery
https://brandonmontgomery.smugmug.com

Maryann T Wehe
Email beachbaby33761@gmail.com
Divine Dream Photography

Nikki Vandiver
https://photoartbynicola.myshopify.com/

Sayword Johnson

Jennifer Cairo

Some images courtesy of shutterstock.com
and depositphotos.com

Soul and sass that one has
You may never see the likes of her again
She's messy and mad
But, oh that heart is home and that mind is magic
Her eyes tell a story of fairytales
and star-filled nights
The kind of love you wish you had . . .